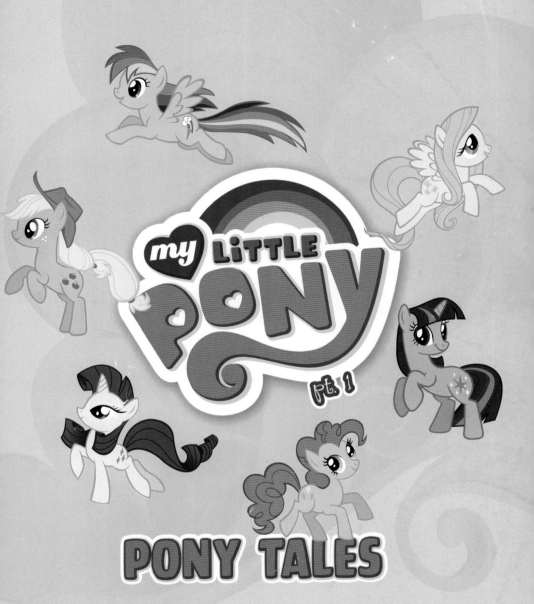

my LiTTLE PONY

pt. 1

PONY TALES

COVER BY *Tony Fleecs*

SERIES EDITS BY *Bobby Curnow*

COLLECTION EDITS BY *Justin Eisinger* AND *Alonzo Simon*

COLLECTION DESIGN BY *Neil Uyetake*

Special thanks to Erin Comella, Robert Fewkes, Joe Furfaro, Heather Hopkins, Pat Jarret, Ed Lane, Brian Lenard, Marissa Mansolillo, Donna Tobin, Michael Vogel, and Michael Kelly for their invaluable assistance.

ISBN: 978-1-63140-136-7   17 16 15 14   1 2 3 4

Licensed By: Hasbro

www.IDWPUBLISHING.com
IDW founded by Ted Adams, Alex Garner, Kris Oprisko, and Robbie Robbins

Ted Adams, CEO & Publisher
Greg Goldstein, President & COO
Robbie Robbins, EVP/Sr. Graphic Artist
Chris Ryall, Chief Creative Officer/Editor-in-Chief
Matthew Ruzicka, CPA, Chief Financial Officer
Alan Payne, VP of Sales
Dirk Wood, VP of Marketing
Lorelei Bunjes, VP of Digital Services
Jeff Webber, VP of Digital Publishing & Business Development

Facebook: **facebook.com/idwpublishing**
Twitter: **@idwpublishing**
YouTube: **youtube.com/idwpublishing**
Instagram: **instagram.com/idwpublishing**
deviantART: **idwpublishing.deviantart.com**
Pinterest: **pinterest.com/idwpublishing/idw-staff-faves**

Twilight Sparkle

STORY, ART, and LETTERS BY
Thomas Zahler

COLORS BY
Ronda Pattison

Rainbow Dash

STORY BY
Ryan K. Lindsay

ART and COLORS BY
Tony Fleecs

LETTERS BY
Neil Uyetake

Rarity

STORY BY
Katie Cook

ART BY
Andy Price

COLORS BY
Heather Breckel

LETTERS BY
Neil Uyetake

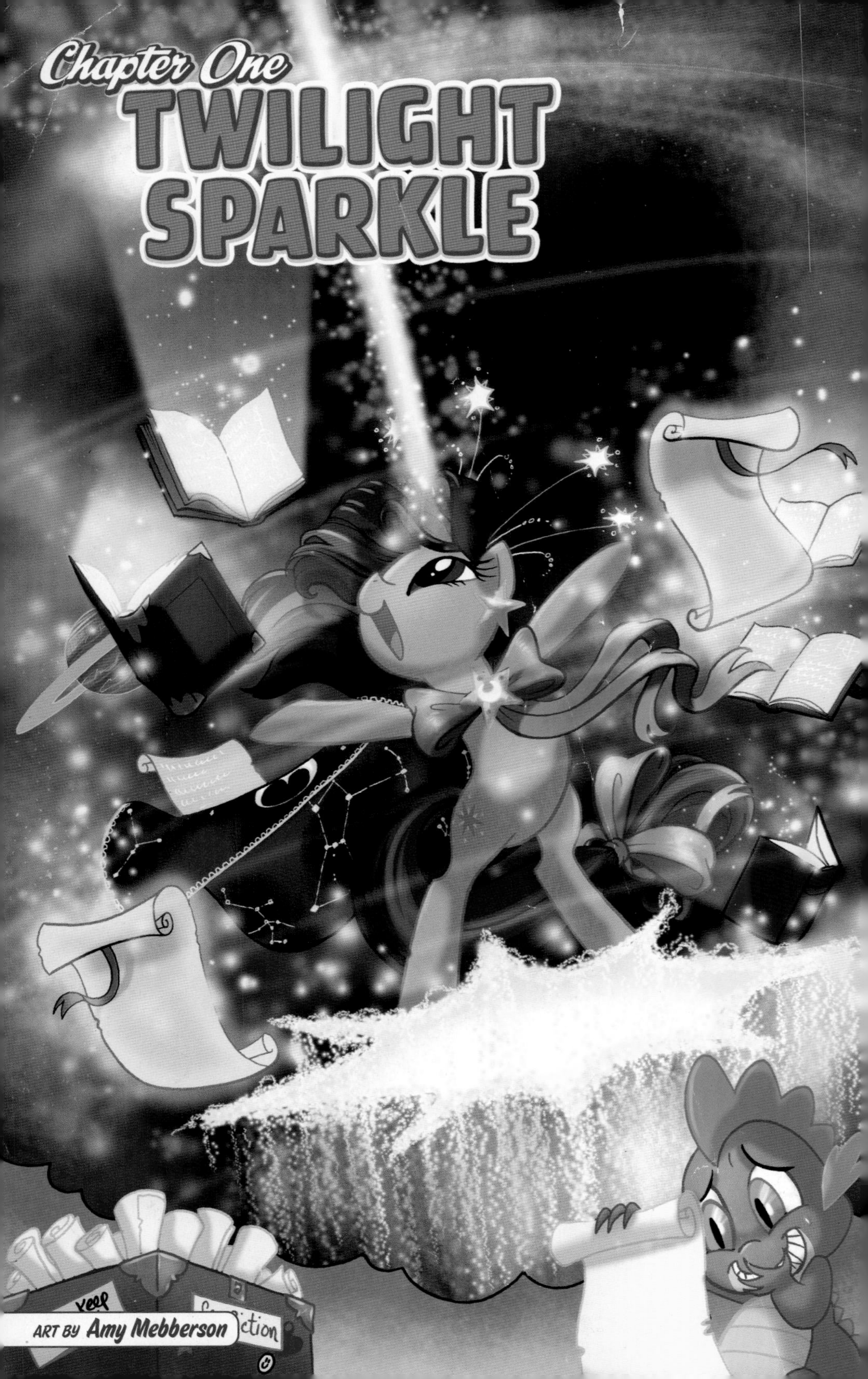
Chapter One
TWILIGHT SPARKLE
ART BY Amy Mebberson

AND WE'VE BEEN STANDING AT THE TOP OF THESE STAIRS FOR ALMOST *HALF AN HOUR.*

I HAPPEN TO *LIKE* THE VIEW OF *CANTERLOT* FROM HERE. AND I—

—OH, *WHO AM I KIDDING?* IT'S ONLY THE *HUGEST TEST* **EVER!**

YEAH, IT'S *PRETTY BAD.* IN FACT, THERE'S ONLY *ONE* THING I CAN THINK OF *WORSE* THAN THAT.

WHAT?

BEING *LATE.*

POOF!

YES, PRINCESS CELESTIA. THAT'S DEFINITELY *ONE WAY* OF LOOKING AT IT.

GREETINGS, TWILIGHT SPARKLE. YOU CERTAINLY SEEM *EXCITED* TO TAKE YOUR TEST.

UNFORTUNATELY, THERE'S BEEN A *CHANGE OF PLANS.*

SUMMER MANE, THE ROYAL ARCHIVIST HAS HAD A *FALL* AND SHE CAN'T GET AROUND.

I NEED TO SEND *SOMEPONY* TO HELP HER UNTIL SHE CAN GET BACK ON HER *HOOVES.*

I WAS THINKING *YOU* MIGHT NOT MIND *POSTPONING* YOUR TEST—

TO GO TO THE *ROYAL ARCHIVES?* THE PLACE WE KEEP COPIES OF ALL OUR BOOKS? *ALL OF THEM?*

I'D SKIP THE TEST *FOREVER* TO SEE THAT!

I THINK A *FEW DAYS* WILL BE ENOUGH.

WHATEVER IT TAKES.

YES, PRINCESS.

THEN LEAVE *RIGHT AWAY*, PLEASE! I'M SURE THE WORK IS *PILING UP*.

I'M *SORRY*, SPIKE, I'M AFRAID I NEED TWILIGHT SPARKLE TO TAKE THIS ON--

--BY *HERSELF*.

THE ROYAL ARCHIVE...

HELLOOOO. IS ANYPONY--

WHO ARE YOU?

ARE YOU *SUMMER MANE?* THE PRINCESS SENT ME TO HELP Y--

DON'T WANT ANY HELP.

SLAM!

CLEARLY.

BUT THE *PRINCESS* ORDERED ME TO--

DON'T CARE.

IT SURE LOOKS LIKE IT MIGHT *RAIN* OUT HERE.

THEN YOU'D BEST *GALLOP BACK* BEFORE IT STARTS.

ALL RIGHT. BUT THE PRINCESS SAID THAT IF YOU *DIDN'T* LET ME IN, I WAS TO LET YOU KNOW THAT THE *NEXT PONY* SHE SENDS WILL BE YOUR *REPLACEMENT.*

FINE.

THOSE ARE *BOOKS.*

DON'T KNOW IF YOU'VE SEEN THEM BEFORE, TWYLEK. YOUNG PONIES THESE DAYS *DON'T READ.*

I KNOW *VERY WELL* WHAT BOOKS ARE. I *LOVE* TO READ!

PROBABLY JUST *COMIC BOOKS,* OR MAYBE THAT SILLY SERIES WITH THE *VAMPIRE PONY*--

FINE, YOU'VE READ THE *TITLES* OF BOOKS. WHO'S YOUR *FAVORITE AUTHOR?*

I READ *EVERYTHING.* I'VE READ DARING DO AND THE QUEST FOR THE SAPPHIRE STATUE, OF PONIES AND PREJUDICE, THE HORSEBACK OF NOTRE DAME--

THAT'S EASY! *JADE SINGER!* SHE WROTE *CANTER IN THE SKY!*

SHE'S A *MYSTERY,* TOO. SHE ONLY WROTE THAT *ONE* BOOK AND THEN *DISAPPEARED.*

BUT *WHAT A BOOK!* IT'S THE *MOST AWESOME*--

--BOOK--

--EVER?

FINE. YOU CAN *READ.* CONGRATULATIONS.

IT'S *LATE.* WE START TOMORROW AT *SIX.*

LET'S SEE *HOW YOU DID*, FLASHLIGHT.

MARE ABOUT YOU... NEIGH OF THE WARRIOR... MARBLE UNIVERSE...

WAIT? *MARBLE UNIVERSE?*

DOESN'T *"M"* COME BEFORE *"N"* IN YOUR ALPHABET, CHILD? *MARBLE UNIVERSE?*

YES, BUT IT'S NOT CALLED *"MARBLE UNIVERSE."* LOOK AGAIN.

"THE *OFFICIAL* HANDBOOK—"

HURM.

YOU'RE RIGHT.

THE OFFICIAL HANDBOOK OF THE **MARBLE UNIVERSE** YOUR GUIDE TO EVERYONE'S FAVORITE METAMORPHIC ROCK

DON'T LET IT *HAPPEN* AGAIN.

YES, MA'AM.

DID YOU—

—EVER—

—NEVER MIND.

WHAT DID—

⫶ULP!⫶

SO, TWYLEK, WHAT ARE YOU READING?

A BIT LATER...

--NO, SHE WROTE THAT ONE OUT *LONGHAND.*

NO WAY! I THOUGHT *EVERYONE* USED A TYPEWRITER.

A *LOT* DO. IN FACT, SOME AUTHORS ARE *VERY PICKY* ABOUT THEIRS.

DO YOU KNOW WHAT *JADE SINGER* USED?

HMM. I THINK SHE USED AN OLD *LIPPONZONER* MODEL. I *DON'T KNOW.*

YOU'RE A LITTLE TOO *HOOKED* ON HER, YOU KNOW. HAVE YOU EVER READ ANYTHING BY *CESIUM GRANDE?*

NO, MA'AM.

IF YOU LIKE SINGER, YOU'LL *LOVE* GRANDE, AND SHE WROTE MORE THAN *ONE OVERRATED BOOK.*

I'LL GET IT FOR YOU--

17

TRY-LIKE?

TRY-LIKE SPACKLE? *WHERE* ARE YOU?

TRY-LIKE?

TRY-LIKE?!

TWILIGHT!!

I'M SORRY! I JUST *OPENED* THE COVER AND THE *NEXT* THING I KNEW—

YOU'RE HERE TO *WORK*, CHILD, *REMEMBER?* LETTING DOWN THE PRINCESS, WHY I *NEVER*—

I'M SORRY! *SO* SORRY!

THE FIRST PARAGRAPH WAS JUST *SO GOOD*, I *COULDN'T* HELP MYSELF.

HAPPENS TO ME *ALL THE TIME*, TWILIGHT.

WHY DO YOU THINK THE BOOKS *PILE UP* AROUND HERE?

--MORE *MACARONI,* TWILIGHT?

YES, PLEASE.

NOW, YOU WERE SAYING...?

IT JUST SEEMS TO ME THAT THE *POINT* OF HAVING ALL THOSE DIVERSE PONIES AT THE END *ISN'T* A TELLING STATEMENT.

IT'S *JUST AS LIKELY* THAT AT THE END OF THE WORLD, A *PEGASUS* WOULD SURVIVE.

THAT'S *VERY* INSIGHTFUL.

THANK YOU. AND IT DOESN'T TAKE AWAY FROM I HAVE NO SNOUT YET I MUST WHINNY BEING A *GREAT BOOK,* OF COURSE.

YOU KNOW, THAT AUTHOR ALSO WROTE *PLAYS* AS WELL.

REALLY? I *DIDN'T* KNOW THAT.

THE NEXT MORNING...

"TWILIGHT, I DECIDED TO HOBBLE INTO *TOWN* AND GET US A *PIE* FOR TONIGHT. THERE'S A *NEW STACK* OF BOOKS THAT NEEDS FILED IN THE *SOUTH WING.*"

HMMMM...

SHE SAID *NOT* TO GO INTO THE OFFICE. *NEVER* GO IN THE OFFICE.

BUT SHE *DIDN'T* SAY I COULDN'T *LOOK* THROUGH THE DOOR IF SHE LEFT IT *OPEN*, RIGHT?

WOW.

I CAN'T BELIEVE I FORGOT MY CHECKBOOK. I--

I--

I *TOLD* YOU TO *STAY OUT OF THE OFFICE!* THE MOST *IMPORTANT RULE* WAS *STAY OUT OF THE OFFICE!*

I *DIDN'T* GO IN. THE DOOR WAS *OPEN* AND--

I'M *SORRY.* I JUST--

GET OUT OF MY SIGHT AND DO *YOUR WORK!*

I'LL DECIDE WHAT TO DO WITH YOU *LATER.*

PACK YOUR THINGS. YOU *LEAVE* IN THE MORNING.

YOU KNOW, I *WASN'T* A LOT OLDER THAN YOU WHEN MY BOOK WAS PUBLISHED. IT WAS A *BIG HIT*.

TOO BIG.

YOU *DON'T KNOW* WHAT IT'S LIKE BEING *THAT GREAT* OUT OF THE GATE.

AND HAVING TO LIVE UP TO THAT A *SECOND TIME*.

BUT *I DO*.

WHEN I TESTED FOR *MAGIC SCHOOL*, I MADE SUCH A SPLASH THAT PRINCESS CELESTIA TOOK ME AS HER *PERSONAL STUDENT*. I HAVE TO LIVE UP TO THAT *EVERY DAY*.

HOW DO *YOU* DO IT?

IT'S *HARD*. BUT THEN I WAS SENT TO PONYVILLE AND I *MADE FRIENDS*, AND THEN IT WASN'T SO BAD. THEY *SUPPORT* ME.

THEY *CELEBRATE* MY VICTORIES AND *CATCH ME* WHEN I FALL.

I *NEVER* HAD *FRIENDS* LIKE THAT.

WELL, YOU DO *NOW*.

ART BY **Sabrina Alberghetti**

Chapter Two
RAINBOW DASH

ART BY **Amy Mebberson**

HERE'S THE MOMENT EVERYPONY'S BEEN WAITING FOR, THE REASON FOR THE SEASON, THE MOMENT OF BLISS THAT LOOKS LIKE THIS...

GO RAINBOW DASH!

...THE WONDERBOLTS!

AND NOW THE LOCAL FAVORITE OF THIS SUMMERFELL FESTIVAL, THE LIGHT REFRACTION OF SATISFACTION...

RAINBOW DASH, WITH HER ALWAYS AMAZING, FOREVER TRAILBLAZING SONIC RAINBOOM!

C'MON NOW, PONY, LET'S GIVE THE CROWD SOMETHING TO REALLY CHEER. LET'S MAKE IT...

200% FASTER

AW, YEAH! THIS IS AWESOME! AWWW...

...NO. SHOULDN'T HAVE PUSHED IT. MY WINGS... I'M OUT OF CONTROL AND I CAN'T AVOID THAT BIG...

...NASTY CLOUD AND...

...

GASP

A NIGHTMARE!

WHAT DO YOU WANT?

TO RAIN ON YOUR PARADE, LITTLE PONY. RUN AND NEVER COME BACK. WE'RE HERE FOR YOUR TEARS AND YOUR BROKEN LITTLE HEART.

WE'LL DRINK UP YOUR SORROW AND FEAST ON YOUR FEAR. WE'VE SWUM IN SADNESS YOU WOULDN'T BELIEVE.

PONIES SOBBING OFF THE SHOULDER OF ORION. WE'VE WATCHED RAINBOWS GLITTER WITH SADNESS NEAR THE TANNHAUSER GATE. ALL THESE MOMENTS WE COLLECT IN TIME, YOUR TEARS OUR RAIN.

LITTLE PONY...

...TIME TO CRY.

AFTER THE FALL OF THE FORTRESS OF THE FANTASTIC.

YOU STUPID CLOUD, WHY DON'T YOU JUST SHOO ON AWAY BACK WHERE YOU'RE WANTED? WHICH IS PROBABLY NOWHERE.

HOW BAD IS IT, APPLEJACK?

BAD ENOUGH I'M THINKING OF PLANTING KIWIS JUST TO GET A CROP. MY GRANNY SMITH WOULD TURN HER SHINY GREEN CHEEK ON ME.

I'M SORRY.

DON'T BE, THIS ISN'T YOUR FAULT.

WELL, MAYBE NOT MY FAULT LIKE WHEN I LOST YOUR BEST SADDLE—

YOU WHAT?

—BUT NONETHELESS THIS TIME I FEEL RESPONSIBLE.

MY WINGS ARE STILL SO TIRED AND NOTHING I'VE TRIED HAS WORKED. I FEEL LIKE THE WORST FRIEND ALIVE.

DON'T FEEL THAT WAY, RAINBOW, I'M SURE—

NO, THAT'S IT, YOU'VE CONVINCED ME...

NO, I WASN'T TRYING—

...I'M GOING TO DO SOMETHING ABOUT THIS TODAY.

LISTEN UP, YOU BIG DUMB CLOUD! I'M COMING FOR YOU...

...AND RAINBOWS ARE COMING WITH ME!

THE TORAINDO.

EPIC.

-TUNK-

FAIL

I'M SORRY.

YEP, THAT ONE WAS YOUR FAULT. WHY DIDN'T YOU WIND IT FASTER?

RAARRRGH, WHY IS THIS SO DIFFICULT? IT'S A CLOUD, IT'S NOT LIKE I'M FIGHTING A NINJA MONSTER MADE OF ALGEBRA AND TANGLED WIRE HANGERS!

A WHAT?

RAARRRGH!

WE ENTER DAY 28 OF CLOUDGATE. YOUNG FILLY, HOW IS THE CLOUD RUINING YOUR LIFE?

EVER SINCE THE CLOUD ARRIVED, EVERYONE'S BEEN DOWN. IT'S LIKE EVERYPONY FORGOT HOW TO BE HAPPY ALL AT THE SAME TIME.

IS THIS CLOUD THE WORST THING TO EVER HAPPEN TO THIS VALLEY?

ABSOLUTELY! I'M PRETTY SURE IT STOLE MY SOCKS OUT OF THE LAUNDRY BASKET. IF A PIG CAN'T LOOK UP THEN DOES IT KNOW WHY WE'RE ALL SAD? I'M COLD—

THIS CLOUD MUST BE AFFECTING YOU THE WORST.

NO, I ACTUALLY KIND OF HEART IT. IT'S TOTES CUTEY.

FIRST TIME RAINBOW FACED THE CLOUD SHE DIDN'T FLY AGAIN FOR A WEEK. SHE'S NOW PULLING HER PUNCHES LIKE A BLOOD SIMPLE PUGILIST ON A LAST NIGHT OF WATERED DOWN GLORY IN THE RING.

SHE'S NOT GONE FASTER THAN A TROT IN SOME TIME WHILE EVERYPONY ELSE GALLOPS INTO FULL BLOWN INESCAPABLE DEPRESSION.

HIS IS RAINBOW DASH'S ROBLEM, AND NOW IS IT ER *FAULT*? SHE SAID SHE OULD SORT IT OUT BUT AS SHE DONE ENOUGH? O YOU FEEL SHE'S RIED EVERYTHING?

I HAVEN'T TRIED EVERYTHING.

NOT EVERYTHING...

...NOT YET.

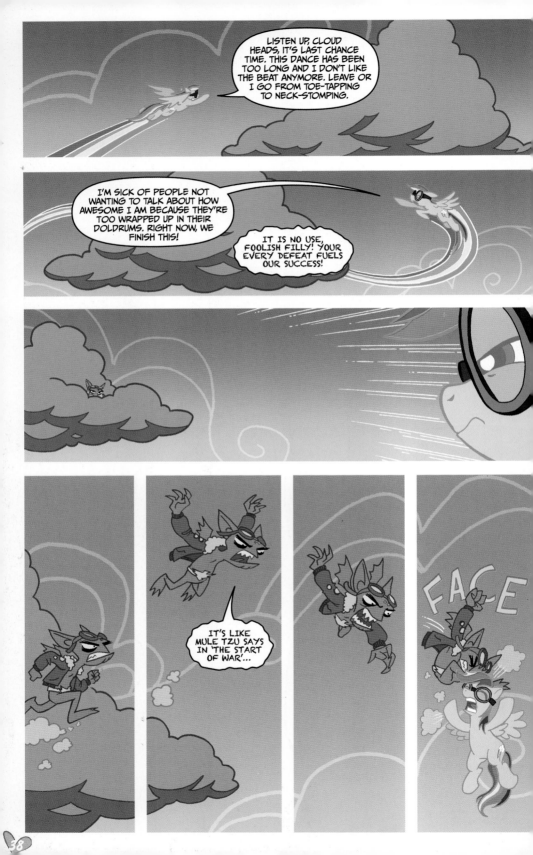

HEY! TAKE YOUR STINKING CLAWS OFF ME, YOU DARN DIRTY GREMLIN!
GET -OOF!
OW! UNCOOL, SO VERY UNCOOL!
DO. NOT. MESS. WITH. US.
AND DON'T GO TOO FAST, WEAK LITTLE PONY, WE WOULDN'T WANT YOU TO RUFFLE THOSE WINGS AGAIN AND HAVE AN OUCHY.

UN. COOL.

THIS IS MY SKY, MY DOMAIN, AND YOU GUYS ARE JUST A BUNCH OF MEAN PASSENGERS. YOU WANT TO GET PHYSICAL? LET'S RUMBLE LIKE IT'S THE APPLE CRUMBLE IN THE JUNGLE!

YOUR FRUSTRATION IS DELICIOUS. THANK YOU.

AND CONSIDER YOUR THREAT IGNORED.

CONSIDER YOUR FACES LAME!

PREPARE TO FIND OUT WHY THE FILLIES LOOK UP TO ME WHETHER I'M IN THE SKY OR NOT.

PREPARE FOR... THE WEB OF RAD DELIGHTS!

ROPE!

SHW

SHW

SHW

SHW

SHW

C'MON, C'MON, C'MON, THIS HAS TO WORK. IT'S A GIANT ROPE WEB, HOW CAN IT POSSIBLY FAIL? IT'S SO AWESOME!

IT'S MAKING THE CLOUD STRONGER AND BIGGER? HOW? THIS IS SO ANNOYING, I HATE THESE GUYS!

DO YOU FEEL THAT? HER DESPERATION, IT'S LIKE...

SWEET MUSIC IN MY BONES.

LET'S FEED ON SUCH SICK MELODY.

41

YUCK, THEY'RE RUINING EVERYTHING. *EVERYTHING!*

GROSS!

KRAKKA

DOOM

PORK CHOPS AND APPLE SAUCE!

TANK, DARLIN', LOOK OUT!

BREAK

PHEW

OH, TANK, I'VE GOT IT! I DON'T HAVE TO CHEER MYSELF UP, I'VE BEEN LOOKING AT IT ALL WRONG. THIS ISN'T ABOUT ME AT ALL—

—WHICH IS REALLY KIND OF WEIRD.

EVEN IF I COULD MAKE MYSELF HAPPY, IT WOULDN'T BE ENOUGH. THAT'S A DROP IN A POND WHEN WE NEED A STORM.

I NEED TO INSPIRE EVERYONE. EVEN MORE THAN I NATURALLY DO EVERY DAY.

IF I CAN MAKE EVERYPONY FEEL HAPPY, EVEN FOR JUST ONE MOMENT, I'LL BE ABLE TO BREAK THE SPELL AND FINALLY GET THE WIN WE ALL KNOW I DESERVE.

IF I'M NOT BACK BY TUESDAY, TELL THE OTHERS I LOVE THEM.

AT 20% FASTER, I LOST CONTROL AND COULDN'T FLY FOR A WEEK. WITH WHAT I'M ABOUT TO DO...

"...I MAY NEVER FLY AGAIN."

SHE'S NEVER GOING TO GIVE UP.

I KNOW, IT'S PERFECT. I COULD DEVOUR HER HATRED FOR YEARS.

SONIC RAINBOOM!

THIS AGAIN? IT DIDN'T WORK THE FIRST TIME, WHY WOULD WE WORRY NOW?

POOR PONY IS GOING TO BE VERY SAD WHEN SHE FAILS. AGAIN.

AHAHAHAHA!

THIS IS EVERYTHING I'VE GOT AND I NEVER SHOULD HAVE GIVEN YOU ANYTHING LESS.

TELL TANK TO POLISH MY TROPHIES EVERY YEAR ON MY BIRTHDAY AND NEVER FORGET ME.

NEVER... FORGET...

FOR THE FIRST TIME IN WEEKS, HAPPINESS WASHES THROUGH THE STREETS. THE NAME *RAINBOW DASH*, FOR THIS MOMENT, IS NO LONGER AN ANNOYED PEJORATIVE BUT A REVERED PRAYER.

AH, THE HAPPINESS! THE GOGGLES, THEY DO NOTHING!

"THE GREMLINS' SPELL WAS BROKEN THROUGH THE COLLECTIVE HAPPINESS OF EQUESTRIA'S PONIES..."

"...BROUGHT ABOUT THROUGH THE WET NOSED DETERMINATION AND SACRIFICE OF ONE PONY WHO COULD NOT GIVE UP."

HOLD ON, WE'RE COMIN'.

"TODAY, EQUESTRIA HONORS AND CELEBRATE A TRUE SELFLESS HERO."

OH, DARLIN'. I DON'T KNOW WHETHER TO KICK YOU OR THANK YOU...

THANK YOU.

...MY... WINGS...

CODA

GET OUT OF BED, YOU ORNERY GALOOT!

DO NOT DISTURB!

WHY?

BECAUSE I BROUGHT YOU A PRESENT! SIZE 9, RIGHT? I FIGURED WITH YOU OUT OF THE SKIES YOU SHOULD FINALLY OWN SOME COMFY SHOES.

THAT'S NOT AS FUNNY AS YOU THINK IT IS.

IT'S FUNNIER!

ORTHOTICS

YOU'RE RIGHT...

I HAVEN'T FLOWN IN TWO MONTHS AND YOU'RE MAKING JOKES? TOO SOON, AJ, TOO SOON!

THIS ISN'T LIKE THE TIME YOU LOST MY SADDLE—

I THOUGHT YOU—

—THIS IS SERIOUS EMOTIONAL BUSINESS.

YOU'RE RIGHT, I'M SORRY, WILL YOU STILL COME FOR A WALK WITH ME?

SCOWL!

NO, I'M SERIOUS. BOOT UP, PONY—WE NEED TO RIDE.

48

WHAT'S THIS?

IT'S OUR LATEST ADVENTURE!

I'M NOT EATING MY BODY WEIGHT IN YOUR APPLES AGAIN, AJ, I WOULDN'T CALL THE EFFECTS FROM THE LAST TIME AN ADVENTU—

DO NOT DISTURB!

APPLE ODYSSEY

NO, SILLY, THESE AREN'T FOR US. WE'RE GOING TO DELIVER THEM.

TO WHOM?

TO EVERYONE.

AND WHAT MAKES YOU THINK EVERYONE'S GOING TO...

...WANT...

I USED APPLES FROM THE CROP YOU SAVED. WE'VE GOT SOMETHING SPECIAL ON OUR HOOVES.

THIS IS DELICIOUS! A PONY COULD FORGET ABOUT FLYING AGAIN IF THESE WERE ON THE GROUND.

I DON'T KNOW HOW IT WORKED, BUT THESE APPLES ARE SOMETHING ELSE, RAINBOW. LITTLE SURPRISE WHEN THEY CAME FROM YOUR VERY BEST.

WHAT DO YOU WANT ME TO DO?

CATCH!

EASY, NEXT?

BRING IT BACK DOWN HERE.

DOWN...?

ART BY **Sabrina Alberghetti**

Chapter Three
RARITY

COME ON, EVERYPONY! PINKIE PIE AND I PUT TOGETHER THE *PERFECT* AFTER PARTY! THERE ARE RADISHES MADE INTO *FLOWERS*!

AND THERE'S A NEW GAME I INVENTED CALLED "PIN THE BUSTLE ON THE BALLGOWN"!

ER... WHAT'S A BUSTLE?

A FEW HOURS LATER...

RARITY! MY GOODNESS, WHERE HAVE YOU BEEN? SPIKE WENT LOOKING FOR YOU OVER TWO HOURS AGO.

OH, JUST MAKING SURE THINGS WERE PERFECT BEFORE I PUT THEM AWAY. SPIKE IS STILL COUNTING THE BEADS ON THE TRIM OF *YAWN* SOMETHING... SOMETHING...

GATOR!!

hic!

I NEED TO MAKE SURE IT'S ALL READY TO SHIP OFF TO CANTERLOT. NOT A STITCH OUT OF PLACE... NO METALLIC ACCENTS TOO... SHINY...

RARITY! EVERYTHING LOOKED PERFECT TONIGHT... YOU'RE MORE THAN READY FOR YOUR BIG SHOW IN CANTERLOT, AND WE'LL ALL BE THERE TO SUPPORT YOU!

YOU'RE WORKING TOO HARD... WHO ARE YOU, TWILIGHT?

RAINBOW!

TOO *HARD?* IF ANYTHING I'M NOT WORKING HARD ENOUGH! THE EXTRAVAGANZA IS... IS...

OH... POOR DEAR. SHE REALLY DOES NEED TO TAKE A BREAK.

AND SHE NEEDS TO BEFORE SHE CRACKS! TRUST ME... I SHOULD KNOW.

HEY YA'ALL! I SAW AN AD IN THE FARMER'S ROWDY WEEKLY ROUND-UP NEWSLETTER THAT JUST MIGHT HELP HER!

THE NEXT MORNING...

THIS IS PERFECT FER' YOU, RARITY! A WEEK AT "FLAX & WHEAT'S NEW AGE ALL-NATURAL WELLNESS CENTER"! WITH A NAME THAT LONG, IT MUST BE FANCY... AND YOU'LL BE BACK GOOD N' RESTED FER' YER SHOW!

OH, I DON'T KNOW IF A WEEK AT A SPA IS SUCH A GOOD IDEA, I HAVE SO MUCH TO DO... HERE, I'M GOING TO PACK SOME OF MY SUPPLIES JUST IN CASE I HAVE A BURST OF INSPIRATION.

DON'T WORRY ABOUT IT. EVERYTHING IS PACKED AND READY TO GO TO CANTERLOT! SPIKE IS TAKING EVERY BOX HIMSELF!

FARMER'S ROWDY WEEKLY Round-UP!

I'M... *HURK* HAPPY TO DO IT FOR YOU, RARITY!

DON'T WORRY ABOUT A THING, RARITY. SPIKE AND I WILL TAKE CARE OF IT ALL. YOU GO RELAX, BE PAMPERED, AND GO TO CANTERLOT REFRESHED AND READY TO SEIZE THE DAY!

SOME PAMPERING WOULD BE NICE...

C'MON...

"MUD ON YOUR FACE," "SAUNAS," "HEALTHY DIET"... THIS IS ALL STUFF YOU LIKE, YOU'LL BE IN HOG HEAVEN!

IT'S AN EXPRESSION.

HOG WHAT?

Boop!

HA!

FARMER'S Round-UP!

PALESCENS

AAAAH!

HONK HONK

FWING!!!

THAT MUST BE THE VALET HERE TO PICK YOU UP!

YOU KNOW, I'M ACTUALLY LOOKING FORWARD TO THIS. IT WILL BE NICE TO RELAX...

55

I'M LOOKING FORWARD TO THIS SLIGHTLY LESS THAN I WAS TWO MINUTES AGO...

HEY, IT'S GOT TWO WHEELS AND ROLLS. IT'LL GET YA' THERE!

...MAYBE.

FLAX & WHEATS

NEW-AGE ALL-NATURAL WELLNES CENTER

DON'T FORGET TO WRITE!

I MEANT TO.

SO... YOU... WORK AT THE RETREAT?

HUH? ER, YEAH! I'M, LIKE, FLAX SEED OF "FLAX AND WHEAT."

FLAX
WHE

ER... SO... YOU... UH... PULL THE WAGON YOURSELF?

WE, LIKE, BELIEVE IN ALL-NATURAL HORSE POWER.

DID YOU KNOW THAT FLAX SEED... THE GRAIN, NOT ME, IS LIKE, BENEFICIAL TO YOUR AURA?

PONYVILLE

WHAT...?

THIS IS A BUMPY ROAD, BUCKLE YOUR BELTS!

I CAN'T! THEY'RE ALL PACKED!

JOSTLE!

BUMP

UH... MR. FLAX, HOW LONG IS THE TRIP?

WHOA, WHOA, WHOA! MR. FLAX WAS MY FATHER. AND NO WORRIES, THREE HOURS AND WE'LL BE, LIKE, CLOSE-ISH.

...

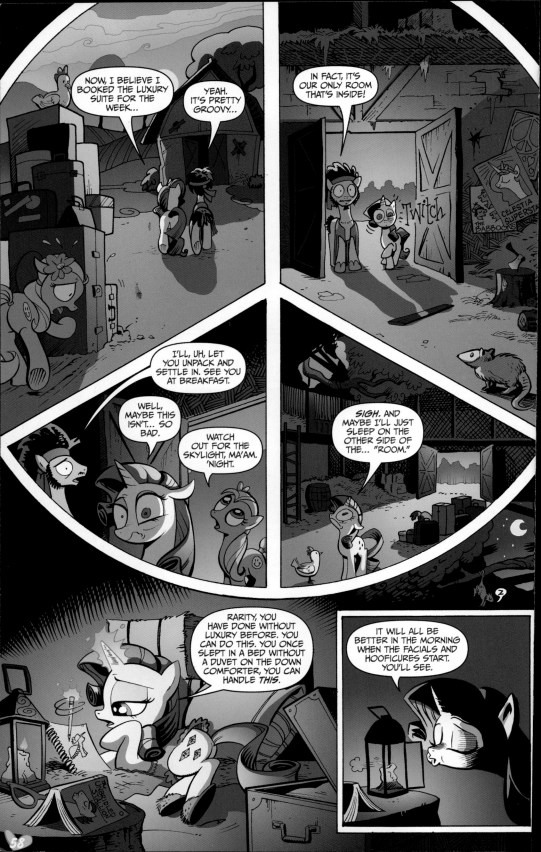

NOW, I BELIEVE I BOOKED THE LUXURY SUITE FOR THE WEEK...

YEAH. IT'S PRETTY GROOVY...

IN FACT, IT'S OUR ONLY ROOM THAT'S INSIDE!

Twitch

THE BABBOONS

CELESTIA SUPERSTAR

I'LL, UH, LET YOU UNPACK AND SETTLE IN. SEE YOU AT BREAKFAST.

WELL, MAYBE THIS ISN'T... SO BAD.

WATCH OUT FOR THE SKYLIGHT, MA'AM. 'NIGHT.

SIGH. AND MAYBE I'LL JUST SLEEP ON THE OTHER SIDE OF THE... "ROOM."

RARITY, YOU HAVE DONE WITHOUT LUXURY BEFORE. YOU CAN DO THIS. YOU ONCE SLEPT IN A BED WITHOUT A DUVET ON THE DOWN COMFORTER, YOU CAN HANDLE *THIS.*

IT WILL ALL BE BETTER IN THE MORNING WHEN THE FACIALS AND HOOFICURES START. YOU'LL SEE.

UNBRIDLED STALLION

NOT A MUD WRAP.

IT'S SOMETHING ALL RIGHT.

WE ARE *REJUVENATING* OURSELVES AND THE EARTH! ISN'T THIS *EXHILARATING?*

ALWAYS LOOK ON THE BRIGHT SIDE...

YES! IT'S... CLARIFYING!

WONDERFUL! YOU'RE GOING TO *LOVE* WHAT'S NEXT!

COMPOST

EXERCISE! THIS IS... MUCH NICER THAN... A NAP. OR A HOOFICURE...

WHAT'S A HOOFICURE?

SIGH...

UGH. I'M SO GLAD THIS DAY IS *FINALLY* OVER! THIS IS THE *WORST...* I'M...

OH! WHAT'S THIS?

"THANK YOU FOR YOUR HARD WORK TODAY. ENJOY THIS JAR OF "GOOPS FOR STUFF: APPLE-CARROT DEEP MANE CONDITIONER."

WELL, A DEEP CONDITIONING *WOULD* MAKE ME FEEL BETTER... AND IT SMELLS HEAVENLY!

YAWN! A DEEP CONDITIONING AND SOME SLEEP. TOMORROW WILL BE A BETTER DAY. *NOTHING* COULD BE WORSE THAN TODAY!

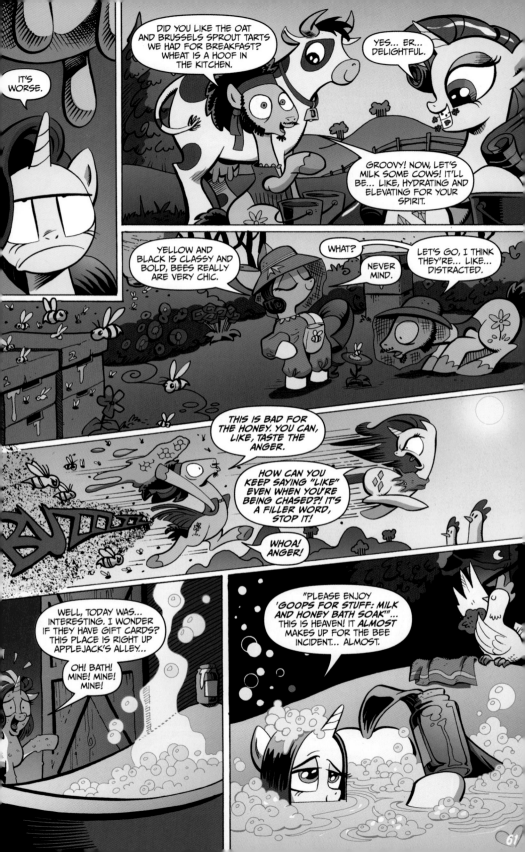

...NOW YOU NEED TO *SEIZE* THE FLOWER BY THE ROOTS AND PULL UP. WE NEED THE WHOLE PLANT!

SEIZE THE DAY... SEIZE THE DAY...

...NO, SEIZE THE ROOTS!

YAWN! THAT BATH WAS POSITIVELY INVIGORATING! I FEEL LIKE I COULD SEIZE THE DAY!

HERE, MY TWIN BROTHER TEMPEH CAN SHOW YOU THE ROPES. THE GREENHOUSE IS HIS DOMAIN!

I... LOVE... GREEN.

WELL, HOWDY! I LOVE GREEN TOO! HEY, DO YOU LIKE SOY?

I... LOVE... SOY.

SOY INKS, SOY MILK, SOY CANDY, SOY OIL, SOY BUTTER...

WELL, *NOW* THINGS ARE LOOKING UP!

YES... SOY... SOY INTERESTING.

EIGHT HOURS OF THE ENTIRE HISTORY OF *SOY.* I SUPPOSE I'VE HAD WORSE FIRST DATES...

THANK CELESTIA, ANOTHER BOTTLE! I WONDER WHAT IT IS THIS TIME... "AFTER TODAY, YOU COULD PROBABLY USE "GOOPS FOR STUFF: ROSEMARY AND HIBISCUS HERBAL HOOF SCRUB", ENJOY!"

NO... NO. MY LABOR CANNOT BE BOUGHT FOR ANOTHER DAY. IN THE MORNING, I'M LEAVING. THIS ISN'T A VACATION, IT'S... IT'S... *MANUAL LABOR!* I HAVE MUCH BETTER THINGS I COULD BE DOING WITH MY TIME GETTING READY FOR THE CANTERLOT EXTRAVAGANZA!

BUC.

BUT FIRST, A HOOF SCRUB.

WE JUST WANTED TO HAVE OUR LITTLE FARM, MAKE OUR "GOOPS" AND LIVE IN NATURE. WE'RE NO GOOD AT THIS "BUSINESS" STUFF... THOSE PONIES BOWLED US OVER AND NOW WE'RE GOING TO LOSE IT ALL. *SIGH.*

OH. WHEAT GRASS, FLAX SEED... I'M SO SORRY.

...AND NOW IT LOOKS LIKE WE MAY HAVE TO GO LIVE IN THE *SUBURBS.* LIKE, MAYBE EVEN *PONYVILLE. GAH!*

EHM. FLAX.

NONE TAKEN.

EH, LIKE, NO OFFENSE?

BUT... THOSE WERE ALL AMAZING!... AND *YOU* MADE THEM... *HERE.* THAT'S INCREDIBLE!

WAIT, DID YOU SAY "MAKE YOUR GOOPS"? ARE YOU TALKING ABOUT ALL THE BEAUTY PRODUCTS YOU'VE BEEN LEAVING IN THE BARN? *YOU* MADE THOSE?

DEAR, WHAT DO YOU THINK YOU'VE BEEN *DOING* HERE? YOU'VE BEEN HELPING TO MAKE THEM YOUR WHOLE VISIT!

THEY AREN'T BEAUTY PRODUCTS... THEY ARE SPIRITUAL ENHANCERS... FOR, LIKE, ENHANCING THE SPIRIT!

WE REALLY DO NEED A BETTER TAGLINE.

SIGH. THAT WAS ACTUALLY THE TAGLINE FOR A WHILE.

HRM. I'VE HEARD OF SUFFERING FOR BEAUTY...

FERTILIZER

POWER TO THE PONIES

MYSTIC CRYSTAL REVELATION

FREAK OUT

KEEP ON TROTTIN'

HARMONY & UNDERSTANDING

MANE THE MUSICAL

HOVERCRAFT

MOTHER

YOU WERE THE *ONLY* PONY THAT REPLIED TO THE WELLNESS CENTER AD. WE'RE OUT OF IDEAS. I'M REALLY GOING TO MISS IT HERE... IT'S OUR HOME. *SNIFF*.

WE'LL THINK OF SOMETHING... LIKE A BETTER TAGLINE. THAT'LL HELP, RIGHT?

FUTURE SITE OF A NEW

ARNYARD ARGAINS

ALWAYS... WATCHING...

COME ON, RARITY. *THINK.* THIIIIINK...

IDEA!

♪

WHEAT GRASS. FLAX SEED. RARITY IS HERE TO *SAVE THE DAY*.

JUST THE DAY? I THINK WE NEED, LIKE, A BUNCH OF DAYS.

RARITY

RIIIGHT. WELL, I CAN HELP! AND I'D LOVE TO HELP YOU. WHAT YOU'RE DOING HERE, NOW THAT I KNOW WHAT IT IS, REALLY IS SOMETHING SPECIAL.

AND IT JUST SO HAPPENS THAT I AM QUITE THE ENTREPRENEUR.

ISN'T ENTREPRENEUR WHAT WE USE ON THE BEETS?

...

WHAT?

I KNOW I PACKED THEM. I THINK THEY WERE UNDER THE CHARMEUSE SILK DAY DRESS... THE ONE WITH THE CAP SLEEVES...

AH, HERE THEY ARE!

AND NOW, IT'S MAGIC TIME! LET'S GET TO WORK AND SAVE YOUR BUSINESS!

Flax & Wheat All Natural Beauty

GATHER ROUND, EVERYPONY! WE HAVE A PLAN ON HOW TO SAVE THIS FARM!

IF THIS WERE A MOVING PICTURE, THIS WOULD BE A GREAT PLACE FOR A MONTAGE!

UNCLE MONTAGE HASN'T WORKED HERE IN YEARS...

FIRST AND FOREMOST, WE WILL NEVER COMPROMISE THE INTEGRITY OF YOUR PRODUCT. IT WILL REMAIN ALL-NATURAL!

INTEGRITY IS, LIKE... IMPORTANT... RIGHT?

67

NEXT, WE REALLY NEED TO... UM, STREAMLINE THE BOTTLING PROCESS. WE CAN'T CREATE BEAUTY IN AN AREA THAT'S NOT BEAUTIFUL!

THIS IS, LIKE, ORGANIZED CHAOS.

PLUS, IT'S REALLY HARD TO FILL SUCH SMALL BOTTLES WHEN YOU DON'T HAVE THUMBS.

WHILE I CAN CERTAINLY APPRECIATE ARTISTIC ORGANIZATION, WE NEED TO MAKE SURE YOU HAVE AS MUCH PRODUCT AS POSSIBLE. NO NEED TO GET YOUR HOOVES DIRTY ANYMORE...

...BECAUSE IT'S ALL *AUTOMATED!* ALL YOU NEED TO DO IS ADD INGREDIENTS AND LABEL THE BOTTLES. ALL OF IT MADE FROM RECYCLED MATERIALS AND ALL OF IT RUNS ON CLEAN ENERGY. *TA DA!*

OH! IT RUNS ON ALL NATURAL HORSE POWER!

JUST LIKE OUR CART!

I *GASP* DON'T KNOW HOW *GASP* CLEAN I'LL BE AFTER A FEW HOURS OF THIS!

BOTTLES

NEXT UP, BRANDING!

BUT, WE ALREADY HAVE CUTIE MARKS!

NOT *THAT* KIND OF BRANDING...

NOW, FLAX SEED, HOW MANY BOTTLES A DAY CAN YOU MAKE OF THE MILK AND HONEY BATH AND HOW MUCH DO YOU CHARGE FOR IT?

WELL, THAT DEPENDS UPON THE *VIBE* I GET FROM THE BEES...

HUMOR ME.

IF THE COWS AND THE BEES ARE, LIKE, IN ALIGNMENT... 11 BOTTLES. AND WE CHARGE 4 BITS FOR IT, DO YOU THINK THAT'S TOO HIGH?

TOO *HIGH?!* IT'S NOT NEARLY ENOUGH! ALL THE WORK THAT GOES INTO IT? NO WONDER YOU CAN'T SUPPORT THE FARM. FROM NOW ON, IT'S 80 BITS A BOTTLE.

80 BITS!? THAT'S... THAT'S UNBELIEVABLE!

NONSENSE. IT'S "EXCLUSIVE." I'D PAY TWICE THAT FOR THIS IN CANTERLOT. WITH YOUR NEW, ALL-RECYCLED MATERIAL PACKAGING AND THE QUALITY OF THE PRODUCT, IT'LL FLY OFF THE... ER, DILAPIDATED TABLE IN FRONT OF YOUR FARM.

FUTURE SITE OF A NEW

THIS MAY NEED SOME COSMETIC WORK.

I'LL GO GET THE HAMMER!

A WHAT?

HIS EYES MOVE WITH ME.

OH! THE WHACK-A-NAIL-INTO-THE-WALL THINGY FOR HANGING PICTURES! MY FRIEND APPLEJACK HAS ONE!

Flax & Wheat

Enchante'

FUTURE SITE
OF A NEW

RARITY! HOWEVER CAN WE THANK YOU? WE'VE ALREADY MADE ENOUGH TO SAVE THE FARM TEN TIMES OVER! WE MAY EVEN GET TO START *PAYING* TOFU AND TEMPEH!

WHOA... LET'S NOT GET CARRIED AWAY WITH OURSELVES HERE...

OH, IT WAS NOTHING. YOU TWO JUST NEEDED A LITTLE HELP... AND YOU REALLY DID NEED TO GET THE AMAZING THINGS YOU CAN MAKE OUT THERE TO ALL OF EQUESTRIA!

THOUGH, IF YOU CAN STAND ONE MORE PIECE OF ADVICE... IF YOU KEEP THE "WELLNESS CENTER" BIT UP, YOU CAN PROBABLY PULL BACK ON THE CRAZY HEALTH FOOD.

OH... THAT WASN'T HEALTH FOOD...

WHEAT GRASS HERE IS JUST A TERRIBLE COOK!

FLAX SEED! YOU REALLY *MUST* COME MEET MY ENTOURAGE. YOU'RE THE NEXT PONY EVERYPONY SHOULD KNOW AFTER ALL!

LIKE, POPULARITY IS A SYSTEM OF RANKING SET UP BY *THE ESTABLISHMENT*...

CHUCKLE ISN'T HE A PIP? DIDN'T I TELL YOU HE WAS A PIP?

...WILL THERE BE FANCY CARROT STICKS?

YES... THE PONY... EVERY... PONY... SHOULD KNOW. *TWITCH*

TWITCH

THANK YOU AGAIN, RARITY. YOU'RE THE BEST PONY.

SIGH... WELL, I'M GLAD THEY'RE HAPPY.

YOU SHOULD BE HAPPY TOO! YOUR FASHION SHOW WAS A COMPLETE SUCCESS! SPIKE TOOK DOWN SO MANY ORDERS, WE RAN OUT OF PARCHMENT!

YES, THIS WHOLE EXPERIENCE *WAS* A TRIUMPH, WASN'T IT? AND, I GOT A LIFETIME SUPPLY OF PLUM & PEAR WITHERS CREAM!

LUNA

Canterlot

CANTERLOT FOR INDOORS

ORDERS

ART BY *Sabrina Alberghetti*

My Little Pony

MORE PONY ADVENTURES!

Get to your nearest retailer
and pick up these books
to add to your stable of
My Little Pony stories!

My Little Pony: Friendship Is Magic, Pt. 1
ISBN: 978-1-61377-628-5

My Little Pony: The Magic Begins
ISBN: 978-1-61377-754-1